FOR Nikki, HARRY ANd JACk

ANNiE MALS

Freddie The Jellyfish

WRITTEN by
EMILY SAMUELS AND MARk RIVLIN

ILLUSTRATED by
Abby EdWARDS

purple
mash
Publishing

So happy to meet you, my name's Annie Mals
My brother is Leo and Lily's my pal.
Today with my family I'm roaming the seas
The weather's so hot, nearly thirty degrees!

Say 'hi' to Freddie, a young jellyfish
He and his friends have only one wish.
To swim in clean water with a view that is clear
And live in the ocean without any fear.

The water's so calm on this hot sunny day
Seagulls are chirping, with plenty to say.
We're watching the fish and enjoying the sun
And learning the names of each single one!

There's Herbert the Haddock and Bertha the Bream
With Eddie the Eel, they make a great team.
I see Florence the Flounder and Charlie the Cod
They all stick together like peas in a pod.

Chatting and swimming, even singing a song
We love to join in while gliding along.
Meeting new fish is very exciting
Last week we found some beautiful whiting.

Whiting are silver with white creamy bellies
They love hanging out with Freddie and the jellies.
Friends playing together is a wonderful sight
But to tell you the truth, something's not right.

It's great to see swimmers and surfers and boats
But not all the rubbish that's left out to float.
Bottles and wrappers and all kinds of packets
A football, a sun hat and badminton racket.

Newspapers, lollies and some rubbish that smells
Cups, plates and spoons with a hamper as well!
Then Freddie the Jellyfish swims over our way
He doesn't look pleased, he's got plenty to say.

'Annie please listen, I'm really unhappy
Walter the Whiting is trapped in a nappy.'
'A nappy?' gasps Lily, 'Like babies wear?'
'Exactly,' says Freddie, 'It should not be there.'

'All these bad things that get dumped in the sea
Are making life hard for my friends and me.
Walter needs help, he's stuck and can't swim.'
'Don't worry,' cries Papa Mals. 'Just lead us to him!'

Mama Mals steers the boat with guidance from Freddie
By the time we reach Walter, Papa Mals is ready.
He puts on his goggles and gets set to dive
Determined to keep our dear Walter alive.

There's so much in the sea that shouldn't be there
For creatures who live here, it's simply not fair.
This junk in the ocean is not good for whiting
For all of these fish, we have to keep fighting.

The sea used to be a home so fantastic
But now it's just dirty, full of old plastic.
If only the people who play on the beach
Would clear their rubbish – that's a lesson to teach.

Sailing back home, we are filled with much sadness
All this pollution is causing such madness.
Lily declares: 'We really have to act fast.
Let's tell the whole world – we can start with our class!'

At school the next day, Miss Kendrick our teacher
Says, 'Caught in a nappy, the poor little creature.
What things can we do to help clean the ocean?
Think of the ways to put wheels into motion!'

'I know', I say, 'We could make up a song.
To put out a message, so loud and so strong!
My big brother Leo is great on guitar
And when he gets older, he'll be a rock star!'

'I can sing!' says Lily. 'I have a good voice.'
'Excellent,' I reply, 'You'll be my first choice.
Let's work together and do all the writing.
We'll make Freddie proud – and Walter the Whiting!'

All through the weekend there's been scorching hot sun
Thousands flock to the beach to swim and have fun.
We've prepared a large board in bright shiny pink
With these words written clearly: 'Please stop and think!'

Everything you bring to the beach on this day
Should go home with you, so please take it away.
Collecting your waste is part of your visit
And helping the world takes less than a minute!

By the late afternoon the beach is so clean
No bottles or nappies, a wonderful scene!
This scorching hot day in early September
Is a day the town will always remember.

The sun's just setting, the water is gleaming
Squeezing my arm Mama Mals says, 'I'm dreaming.'
And then we all witness a magical sight
That brings tears to our eyes as day becomes night.

The whiting and jellies come close to the beach
Then Freddie steps up – he's prepared a short speech.
'Thank you my friends, you've helped us to smile
And that hasn't happened for a very long while.

Annie, your family and friends in the class
Would not allow this big problem to pass.'
Then Lily and Leo climb up on the boat
And everyone sings the song that we wrote.

How good does it feel to be helping the fish?
The lyrics are simple, join in if you wish.
Saving the oceans is a very big task
Let's start with clean beaches – it's not much to ask.

(To be sung to the tune of Row, Row, Row Your Boat)
Please, please take your mess
And leave the beaches clean.
Keep the seas so blue and clear
This is Freddie's dream!

People live on the land
And fish live in the sea.
Everyone needs a home
Happy as can be!

Jellyfish – Fun Facts:

1. There are many jellyfish that glow in the night
    They look amazing with their faces so bright.

2. Here for around six-hundred-million years
    Jellies were the earth's first living pioneers.

3. Although they are missing blood, brains, and heart
    Jellies move with vibrations – now that's really smart!

4. Jellyfish can be found all over the planet
    Oceans and seas are places they inhabit.

5. Jellies are like jelly, they don't have a spine
   But the way that they swim is perfectly fine!

6. They are not always friendly, sometimes they sting
   Put vinegar on the wound, it sorts everything!

7. Some jellyfish have incredible tentacles
   Thirty metres long, that's a great spectacle!

8. Jellies are called Flower Hats and Blue Blubbers
   Also Pink Meanies, can you think of some others?

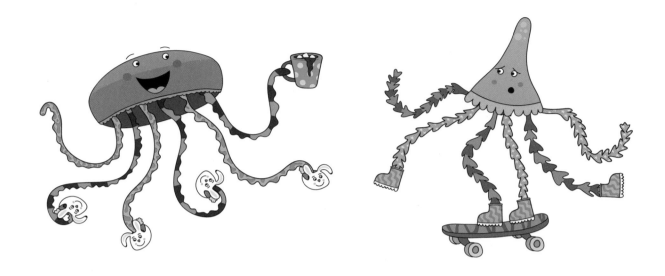

Published by Purple Mash Publishing (an imprint of 2Simple Publishing)
5 Broadbent Close, London, N6 5JW, UK
Company number 08608270

Editor: Cheryl Moskowitz

ISBN 978-1-7398251-4-0
Printed in the UK by Pollards Print, 2022